THE MUSICIANS LIBRARY

EIGHTY-FOUR VOLUMES ISSUED

SONG VOLUMES*

JOHANNES BRAHMS: FORTY SONGS
Edited by James Huneker

ROBERT FRANZ: FIFTY SONGS
Edited by William Foster Apthorp

EDVARD GRIEG: FIFTY SONGS
Edited by Henry T. Finck

GEORGE FRIDERIC HANDEL
VOL. I. SONGS AND AIRS FOR HIGH VOICE
VOL. II. SONGS AND AIRS FOR LOW VOICE
Edited by Ebenezer Prout

ADOLF JENSEN: FORTY SONGS
Edited by William Foster Apthorp

FRANZ LISZT: THIRTY SONGS
Edited by Carl Armbruster

FRANZ SCHUBERT: FIFTY SONGS
Edited by Henry T. Finck

ROBERT SCHUMANN: FIFTY SONGS
Edited by W. J. Henderson

RICHARD STRAUSS: FORTY SONGS
Edited by James Huneker

P. I. TCHAÏKOVSKY: FORTY SONGS
Edited by James Huneker

RICHARD WAGNER: LYRICS FOR SOPRANO
Edited by Carl Armbruster

RICHARD WAGNER: LYRICS FOR TENOR
Edited by Carl Armbruster

RICHARD WAGNER: LYRICS FOR BARITONE AND BASS
Edited by Carl Armbruster

HUGO WOLF: FIFTY SONGS
Edited by Ernest Newman

. .

FIFTY MASTERSONGS
Edited by Henry T. Finck

FIFTY SHAKSPERE SONGS
Edited by Charles Vincent

MODERN FRENCH SONGS
VOL. I. BEMBERG TO FRANCK; VOL. II. GEORGES TO WIDOR
Edited by Philip Hale

MODERN RUSSIAN SONGS
VOL. I. ALPHERAKY TO MOUSSORGSKY
VOL. II. MOUSSORGSKY TO WIHTOL
Edited by Ernest Newman

ONE HUNDRED ENGLISH FOLKSONGS
Medium Voice
Edited by Cecil J. Sharp

ONE HUNDRED FOLKSONGS OF ALL NATIONS
Medium Voice
Edited by Granville Bantock

ONE HUNDRED SONGS BY TEN MASTERS
VOL. I. SCHUBERT, SCHUMANN, FRANZ, RUBINSTEIN & JENSEN
VOL. II. BRAHMS, TCHAÏKOVSKY, GRIEG, WOLF, AND STRAUSS
Edited by Henry T. Finck

ONE HUNDRED SONGS OF ENGLAND
Edited by Granville Bantock

SEVENTY SCOTTISH SONGS
Edited, with accompaniments, by Helen Hopekirk

SIXTY IRISH SONGS
Edited by William Arms Fisher

SIXTY PATRIOTIC SONGS OF ALL NATIONS
Medium Voice
Edited by Granville Bantock

SONGS BY THIRTY AMERICANS
Edited by Rupert Hughes

SIXTY FOLKSONGS OF FRANCE
Medium Voice
Edited by Julien Tiersot

SONGS FROM THE OPERAS FOR SOPRANO
SONGS FROM THE OPERAS FOR MEZZO SOPRANO
SONGS FROM THE OPERAS FOR ALTO
SONGS FROM THE OPERAS FOR TENOR
SONGS FROM THE OPERAS FOR BARITONE AND BASS
Edited by H. E. Krehbiel

PIANO VOLUMES

JOHANN SEBASTIAN BACH
VOL. I. SHORTER PIANO COMPOSITIONS
VOL. II. LARGER PIANO COMPOSITIONS
Edited by Ebenezer Prout

LUDWIG VAN BEETHOVEN: VOLS. I & II. PIANO COMPOSITIONS
Edited by Eugen d'Albert

JOHANNES BRAHMS: SELECTED PIANO COMPOSITIONS
Edited by Rafael Joseffy

FRÉDÉRIC CHOPIN: FORTY PIANO COMPOSITIONS
Edited by James Huneker

FRÉDÉRIC CHOPIN: THE GREATER CHOPIN
Edited by James Huneker

S. COLERIDGE-TAYLOR: TWENTY-FOUR NEGRO MELODIES
Transcribed for the piano

EDVARD GRIEG: LARGER PIANO COMPOSITIONS
Edited by Bertha Feiring Tapper

EDVARD GRIEG: PIANO LYRICS AND SHORTER COMPOSITIONS
Edited by Bertha Feiring Tapper

FRANZ JOSEPH HAYDN: TWENTY PIANO COMPOSITIONS
Edited by Xaver Scharwenka

FRANZ LISZT: TWENTY ORIGINAL PIANO COMPOSITIONS
Edited by August Spanuth

FRANZ LISZT: TWENTY PIANO TRANSCRIPTIONS
Edited by August Spanuth

FRANZ LISZT: TEN HUNGARIAN RHAPSODIES
Edited by August Spanuth and John Orth

FELIX MENDELSSOHN: THIRTY PIANO COMPOSITIONS
Edited by Percy Goetschius

WOLFGANG AMADEUS MOZART: TWENTY PIANO COMPOSITIONS
Edited by Carl Reinecke

FRANZ SCHUBERT: SELECTED PIANO COMPOSITIONS
Edited by August Spanuth

ROBERT SCHUMANN: FIFTY PIANO COMPOSITIONS
Edited by Xaver Scharwenka

RICHARD WAGNER: SELECTIONS FROM THE MUSIC DRAMAS
Arranged for the piano by Otto Singer

. .

ANTHOLOGY OF FRENCH PIANO MUSIC
VOL. I. EARLY COMPOSERS; VOL. II. MODERN COMPOSERS
Edited by Isidor Philipp

ANTHOLOGY OF GERMAN PIANO MUSIC
VOL. I. EARLY COMPOSERS; VOL. II. MODERN COMPOSERS
Edited by Moritz Moszkowski

EARLY ITALIAN PIANO MUSIC
Edited by M. Esposito

MODERN RUSSIAN PIANO MUSIC
VOL. I. AKIMENKO TO KORESTCHENKO
VOL. II. LIADOFF TO WRANGELL
Edited by Constantin von Sternberg

*All song volumes are issued for both High and Low Voice, except where otherwise stated.

MODERN RUSSIAN SONGS
VOLUME I

MODERN
RUSSIAN SONGS

EDITED BY ERNEST NEWMAN
VOLUME I
ALPHERAKY TO MOUSSORGSKY

FOR LOW VOICE

THE
MUSICIANS
LIBRARY

BOSTON: OLIVER DITSON COMPANY

NEW YORK: CHAS. H. DITSON & CO. CHICAGO: LYON & HEALY

D. B. UPDIKE, THE MERRYMOUNT PRESS, BOSTON

CONTENTS

CONTENTS

INDEX

INDEX

BALAKIREFF

BLEICHMANN

ARENSKY

CUI

EIGHT

RUSSIAN

COMPOSERS

IPPOLITOFF-IVANOFF

GLINKA

GRETCHANINOFF

BORODINE

THE RUSSIAN SONG

THE thesaurus of Russian song is the second richest in Europe in one respect, and the first in another. Every country has, of course, an abundance of musical lyrics. But it will hardly be disputed by any one that the Germanic races have produced the largest number of art songs of the highest class; and it will probably be admitted by every one who has given any study to the subject that the Russian treasury of song surpasses even the German in variety, if not in quantity. Vast as the German output has been, and varied as have been the minds that have expressed themselves in the song, the family likenesses overbear, on the whole, the personal differences: there is an unmistakable something that is common to Schubert, Schumann, Brahms, Wolf, Jensen, Franz, Strauss, Mahler, and a hundred others. These family likenesses, it is true, will be found in the songs of every race, and it goes without saying that they exist in the Russian song. None the less true is it, I think, that the personal characteristics are more marked there than in the German song: to pass from Glinka to Borodine, from Borodine to Moussorgsky, from Moussorgsky to Rachmaninoff, from Rachmaninoff to Stravinsky, from Stravinsky to Arensky, from Arensky to Liapounoff, from Liapounoff to Medtner, from Medtner to Vassilenko, from Vassilenko to Tchaïkovsky, from Tchaïkovsky

to Tcherepnin, and so on through a score of other names, is to see a more sharply differentiated set of physiognomies than when we pass from Schubert to Schumann, from Schumann to Mahler, from Mahler to Strauss, from Strauss to Wolf, from Wolf to Loewe. And the remarkable thing is that this unusually rich crop of song has been sown and reaped in much less than a century. There were Russian and pseudo-Russian song composers before Glinka: one pre-Glinka song, the "Nightingale" of Alabieff (1802–1852), is still occasionally sung. But to all intents and purposes the Russian song begins with Glinka (1804–1857). The earliest of his songs date from his teens, but the bulk of them—and certainly the best of them—were written after he was thirty: of the two included in the present collection, "The Star of the North" belongs to 1839, "The Journey" to 1840. ("A Life for the Czar," it will be remembered, was produced in 1836, and "Rousslan and Ludmilla" in 1842.) Schubert's "Erl King" was written in 1815, and there had been a long and honorable line of German song composers before Schubert; a masterpiece like the "Erl King," indeed, could come only as the crown of a long tradition, whereas even the best songs of Glinka are no more than a beginning.

II

THE variety of style of the Russian song is the result of the variety of influences, racial, local, and cultural, to which it has been subject. German art song has drunk as deeply of the fountain of folksong; but German art music and German folk music have always been so intimately associated that it is hard to say where the one ends and the other begins. It is not so much that the folk music has been an influence upon the composers as that

it has been part of their bone and blood and being. The moods, the prosody, the structure, the cadence of the folksong run, broadly speaking, through almost all the German music, sacred and secular, vocal and instrumental, of the last three hundred years. The music and the poetry of the race developed hand in hand. We have only to turn over a German anthology of poetry to see that the poetic rhythms of five hundred years ago, whether they be those of folk poets or of art poets, are the same as those of Heine and Goethe and Heyse and Eichendorff and Dehmel; and until Hugo Wolf enlarged the rhythmic boundaries of the German song, it followed, in general, the metrical models of the folksong of centuries ago.

In Russia the evolution was different. Russian folk music had existed long before Russian art music came into being; with the result that when the composers fell under its spell, it became a genuine *influence* of which they were more or less conscious. Art music as the German musician of the mid-nineteenth century knew it could not go to the German folksong for inspiration, for it had never really quitted it. But the Russian composer who, having learned his technique and imbibed a good part of his idiom from the Western music of his day, turned then to his native folk music, found in it an inexhaustible treasure-house of novelty. Thus we can speak of a genuine *influence* of Russian folksong upon Russian art song.

III

RUSSIAN music, again, was fortunate in that it had no national cultural tradition of its own so overwhelming that there was no escape from it — no thought of escape from it. German music, on the whole, has been self-contained for many generations: each young composer has drunk in the one great German tradition as naturally and unconsciously as he breathed in the German air. The tradition, the culture, were uniform for the whole political area. The Russian escaped this uniformity of influence. On the one hand, as we have seen, there were the treasures of folksong to draw upon. On the other, there was, in addition to marked local differences of race and tradition, a strong Oriental or quasi-Oriental influence. A Croatian composer like Haydn, a Bohemian composer like Gluck, are drawn so deeply into the German tradition that they are, in essence, German composers pure and simple. But the Orientalism that has always been part of Russian music has never lost its own characteristics of mood and style; neither it nor the Russian folk style has ever been strong enough to absorb the other. The Russian song composer thus already has two sources of culture to draw upon, as against the German's one; and in addition he has —the German culture. Like his country, he is both in Europe and apart from it. He has his own inner sources of spiritual strength, and he is free to assimilate what he will of the spiritual strength of the rest of Europe. And in music this has meant, in the main, taking the best that the great Germans could give him.

IV

THUS we get three different styles in the Russian song,—the folk style, the Oriental style, and the style that is a distillation from the German song. Sometimes the three are exploited separately; more often they are subtly interblended. (Other styles also are found, but they are personal rather than communal—the quasi-recitative of Dargomijsky, for instance, the Moussorgsky songs that get as close as possible to the rhythms and accents of speech, and the post-impressionist style, as we may perhaps call it, of the later Stravinsky. These are not represented in the present volumes.)

From the beginning the Russian song showed a good deal of variety. Glinka has one ear always open to folksong; but he never quite forgets the suave Italian style in which he was brought up. His successor Dargomijsky fluctuates between Italianism, Orientalism, Muscovitism, eclecticism, and something that is absolutely his own. The "Five" (Cui, Borodine, Rimsky-Korsakoff, Moussorgsky, and Balakireff) exhibit far more variety than the contemporary German song can show. When the nationalist impulse of the '50s and '60s weakened, Russian song composers went each his own way, some of them still writing deliberately in the folk style, others feeling the folk style more or less unconsciously as a stimulus, still others, like Medtner, ignoring it completely. Only the theorist will cry out against composers of this last type. The plain man will decide that it does not matter in the least in what style a musician writes, so long as it is a good style. An artist can express finely only what he has felt deeply; and if a composer finds himself more responsive to the culture of another nation than to the popular life of his own, we have no right to say him nay. If it is objected that Medt-ner's songs are not Russian but German, the sufficient answer is that, whatever section of the map they may set us thinking about, they are first-rate. No doubt a German might have written them, but as a matter of fact no German did; and it is better for us that they should have been written by a Russian than not written at all. A man must be allowed to choose his own loves and friendships in art as in private life. If Medtner prefers to spend his time talking to Goethe and Heine and Brahms and Wolf, rather than in freezing his toes watching the Russian peasant doing his frog dance in the snow, that is purely his affair. To do anything else would be insincerity on his part; and out of insincerity no great art can come.

V

MEDTNER shows practically no trace of "nationalism." Most of the others exhibit it in one form or another, one degree or another. Sometimes a song is deliberately couched in the folk idiom: perhaps the most thoroughgoing example of this in the present collection is the "Parrot Song" of Moussorgsky (from *Boris Godounoff*)—which is none the less a song for being contained in an opera. Sometimes we are conscious of the Russian people in the song, even though the phrases may not, in the main, specifically copy the folk style; the suggestion is psychological rather than tonal. To this class belong Moussorgsky's "Savishna" and "Gathering Mushrooms;" they bring up Russia before our eyes, not so much by the use of external apparatus, such as scales or cadences, but by painting the folk from the life. In this sphere, indeed, Moussorgsky still stands alone. No composer in any country has been so thoroughly of the people in his sympathies and in his art. For Moussorgsky, folksong was not, as it is for most composers, an exotic, a *sauce piquante*, with which to dash the common musical idiom now and then, but the expression of the very soul of the people—not the people as the town-dweller sees them, half sympathetically, half condescendingly, but as they see themselves. Moussorgsky felt their few joys and their many sorrows as no other composer has done; and the intensity of his absorption in them made him speak their own musical tongue, but speak it as a genius of the people would do.

He had the painter's eye and the novelist's breadth of sympathy. He joined hands on one side with Verestchagin, on the other with Dostoievsky. His was the period of intense national consciousness and aspiration, of sympathy on the part of the intelligentsia with the poor and oppressed. The "Savishna" is a human document without an analogue in any other song literature. One day, from the window of the country house in which he was staying, he looked out of the window and saw the village idiot begging the love of the village beauty, and being repulsed with scorn for his hideousness and poverty. The wave of pity that surged through Moussorgsky found voice in "Savishna;" the words as well as the music are his. The song is, on the whole, the finest example of his realism. He has hit upon a $\frac{5}{4}$ rhythm that well expresses the urgency of the peasant's appeal: the absence of a single quaver's rest anywhere in the song suggests the panting breathlessness of his long cry; and it finishes without a formal ending,—the breath just goes out of him, and that is the end, with the song still suspended, question-like, in the air.

VI

MOUSSORGSKY gives us better than any one else both the direct imitation of folksong and the sublimation of this into art song. Of the latter, the finest specimens, apart from "Savishna," are "Gathering Mushrooms" and the "Hopak." Here the slight touch of peasant harshness that we are conscious of in such songs as the "Trepak" disappears. These songs, too, are better built than some of the realistic ones: they have a perfection of form—particularly "Gathering Mushrooms"—that reminds us of the greatest German songs.

The folksong influence, as I have said, shows itself in various ways in the other composers. The folk style will always be found, employed deliberately, when the Russian people are the subject of the poem. We see it, for instance, in Cui's "Hunger Song," Kopyloff's "The Laborer's Plaint," and Wihtol's "Beggar's Song." Russian popular song has often a curious monotony of phrase, as if the idea in the singer's mind were an obsession, as if the complete giving up of the soul to the one feeling had almost numbed the faculty of speech. It is with this monotony, this hammering on the one idea, that Moussorgsky and the other writers of the song of social sympathy, as we may call it, make their most poignant effects.

In other cases the folk idiom enters quite unconsciously into the style of the composer, as a local peculiarity of accent will sometimes show in the speech of a man who otherwise speaks the standardized tongue of the capital. It is the purely Russian touch that we get, for example, in measures 7 and 8 of Bagrinofski's "All the Bells;" and the reader will detect a hundred other touches of the same kind in other songs. Often the Russian flavor comes from peculiar rhythms that are not found in the songs of any other race; these rhythms in their turn are conditioned by the prosody and inflections of the language.

The influence of the build of a language upon the rhythms of the music of a country has never been sufficiently investigated. It is tolerably clear that one of the most familiar phrase-endings of Spanish music—this, from Granados's "Goyescas"—

has come into being through the richness of the Spanish language in double rhymes,—*muerto, cierto, amante, anhelante, amores, flores, mundo, profundo,* and so on. The process may be seen at work in the following passages from Granados's songs "La Maja dolorosa:"

Double rhymes being scarce in English (except in present participles), it is not surprising that this peculiar effect, as of the shooting of the same bolt upon a pair of phrases, is not one of the characteristics of English melody.

Russian prosody has had a good deal of influence on Russian melody. Russian poetry is rich in dactylic endings—which, needless to say, set the English translator insoluble problems at times. These dactyls often end in a vowel—another thorn in the side of the translator, for the vowel-ending gives a peculiar lightness to the finish of the Russian phrase that cannot be duplicated in English. I once had this forcibly brought home to me by hearing a Czech choir sing "God save the Queen" (in their own tongue). Each two-measure phrase tapered off like the thin end of a wedge; with us, from the very nature of the words, the emphasis on each note is the same. The difference between the all-through blunt effect and the tapering effect in the dactyl may be illustrated by the unvarying lumpishness of the consonantal "gracious Queen" or "walking-stick"—which some people would not even class as dactyls, but as feet of three longs—and the airiness, the dive and float, of "Arcady" or "mystery."

With these illustrations in mind, let the reader now look at Liapounoff's "Christmas Song." The Russian text of the first eight measures, corresponding to the English words—

> " *Little song of Christmastide,*
> *Tuneful in its dulcet sound*
> *Like unto a string of pearls*
> *Radiant on a velvet ground,*"

may be roughly transliterated thus—

It will be seen that the most expert choice of English words cannot quite reproduce the lilt of the original, the soft vowel-endings of the lines, the tapering of the verbal sound that suggests to the singer a corresponding tapering of the melodic phrase. The geniuses of the two languages are absolutely different. I draw attention to the fact here not only to show how gallantly the translators have braved these and other difficulties, but to indicate, *en passant,* the correct phrasing (because the natural phrasing) of the melodies, and to show how, in many cases, a type of melody that strikes the ear at once as being peculiarly Russian has come about not through any conscious desire of the composer to imitate a folk idiom, but purely and simply as the result of the "pull" of the words.

The same phenomenon is met with again in Kalinnikoff's "Stars Ethereal," where the opening Russian words run thus (two measures to a line):

> *Zvezdi yasneya, zvezdi prikrasniya*
> *Nashentali tsvetam skazki choodniya.*

Vocal rhythms such as those of Tcherepnin's "Stars of Radiant Night" and Moussorgsky's "Ah, not with God's Thunder," again, will not be found in the songs of any other race: they are motived and conditioned by the genius of the Russian language.

VII

WITH these general remarks on the style and the scope of the Russian song, the reader may now be left to find his own enjoyment in working through the present volumes. There is something for all tastes. Even on what may be called, without offence, the lower slopes, the vintage is better than in most countries. There is always room for the song that, without any pretence of profundity of philosophy or science of technique, gives voice to the simple, honest feelings of simple, honest people. There is no need for this sort of thing to degenerate into the bleating sentimentality of the worst German, the anaemic thinness of the worst French, or the devastating vulgarity of the worst English song. Men like Alpheraky can be popular without being inane. The cosmopolitan Russian composers, such as Arensky, Taneieff, Rubinstein, Tchaïkovsky, and Gretchaninoff, still have a Russian touch somewhere or other about them. Medtner falls into line with the greatest of the German song writers: Hugo Wolf himself would not have disdained to sign a song like "Solitude." Liapounoff, like Medtner, is an accomplished writer for the piano, and his accompaniments profit by his double gift. Rimsky-Korsakoff exhibits in his songs the same range of interests, the same variety of styles, and the same sensitiveness to beauty, as in his operas and instrumental works. Rachmaninoff, like Medtner and Liapounoff, fertilizes his lyric style by his genius for the piano, and limns his peculiarly serious physiognomy as unerringly in his smaller as in his larger works. Tcherepnin, Vassilenko, and Sachnofsky illustrate some of the newer phases of the Russian song, with its surety of technique placed at the service of a generous eclecticism of interest. Stravinsky is represented by a song of his youth, in which the discriminating ear can catch many a prophecy of the later Stravinsky. All in all, the songs here presented give, it is hoped, an adequate idea of the extraordinary richness of a development that has been crowded into but little over three quarters of a century,—the most marvellous record that the song can show in any European country in the same space of time.

Ernest Newman.

BIOGRAPHICAL SKETCHES

ALPHERAKY, ACHILLES NIKOLAIEVITCH
Born at Charkov, June 21, 1846. Was at one time attached to the Czar's court. He has written an opera, piano pieces, songs, etc.

ARENSKY, ANTON STEPANOVITCH
Born at Novgorod, July 31, 1861. Both his parents were musical. After some preliminary studies under Zikke, he entered Rimsky-Korsakoff's class at the Petrograd Conservatoire (1879–82); in the latter year he was appointed professor of harmony and counterpoint at the Moscow Conservatoire. He became conductor of the Russian Choral Society's concerts in Moscow, and, in 1895, of the Imperial Chapel Choir in Petrograd. He died on February 12, 1906. His works include the successful opera, *A Dream on the Volga* (1890), two other operas, *Raphael* (in one act, 1894) and *Nal and Damayanti* (1899), various cantatas and choruses, much church music, two symphonies, a piano concerto, a piano trio, two string quartets, a piano quintet, a ballet (*Egyptian Night*), a large number of piano pieces and songs, and two books, on harmony and form, respectively.

BAGRINOFSKI, M.

BALAKIREFF, MILI ALEXEIVITCH
Born at Nijni-Novgorod, January 2, 1837. He received his first lessons in music from his mother. In his youth he lived for a time in the country house of Oulibicheff, the biographer of Mozart and author of a book on Beethoven. Oulibicheff had an extensive musical library and maintained a private band, by both of which the student and budding composer profited; he was deeply impressed also by the peasant music of the province. He went to live in Petrograd in 1855, met Glinka, and was soon regarded by the latter—then approaching the end of his days—as his destined successor in the renaissance of Russian music. Gradually Balakireff gathered about himself a number of young enthusiasts inspired by the same nationalistic ideals: a group of five (Balakireff himself, Cui, Moussorgsky, Rimsky-Korsakoff, and Borodine) became known as "The Invincible Band," and worked in harmony for some years, until the varying temperaments of its members led to a certain divergence from each other. Balakireff was an erudite musician and a skilled technician; his influence upon the rest of the group was great.

In 1862 he helped to found the Free School of Music in Petrograd; its concerts were intended to be a progressive counterblast to the more conservative work of the Imperial Musical Society. In 1869 he became conductor of the latter Society and Director of the Imperial Chapel Choir. He retired from the directorship of the Free School of Music in 1873, being succeeded by Rimsky-Korsakoff; from that date until his death at Petrograd, on May 29, 1916, he lived in more or less seclusion, his mind having taken on a markedly mystical cast.

He is best known by his symphonic poem *Thamar*, the piano piece *Islamey*, the *Overture on Russian Themes*, and a symphonic poem *Russia* (written in 1862 for the celebration of the thousandth anniversary of the Russian nation). In addition he wrote an overture to *King Lear*, an *Overture on Czech Themes*, two symphonies, a piano concerto (his last work), a number of piano pieces, and some songs. He also edited two collections of Russian folksongs.

BLEICHMANN, JULIUS IVANOVITCH
Born at Petrograd, December 5, 1868. Studied at the Conservatoire there under Solovieff and Rimsky-Korsakoff; afterwards under Reinecke and Jadassohn in Leipzig. He founded (1893–94) the Petrograd Popular Symphony Concerts and was conductor of the Philharmonic Concerts (1894–95). Died in Petrograd December 5, 1909. His works include two operas, piano pieces, chamber music, orchestral works, songs, etc.

BORODINE, ALEXANDER PORPHYRIE-VITCH
Born at Petrograd, October 31, 1834,— the illegitimate son of a Prince of Imeritia (Georgia). His scientific bent asserted itself at an early age. It was decided that he should take up medicine as a career, and to that end he entered the Petrograd Academy of Medicine. In 1856 he received an appointment as surgeon in an army hospital, where he first met Moussorgsky, though the friendship did not ripen till the pair met again after some three years' separation. He took his degree in 1858, and spent from 1859 to 1862 travelling in various European countries at the expense of the Russian Government, studying different medical methods. On his return, in 1862, he was appointed assistant lecturer at the Petrograd Academy of Medicine. His friendship with Balakireff, who influenced him strongly, dates from about this time. He married in 1863, became a lecturer in chemistry, and helped to found the School of Medicine for Women, at which institution he lectured from 1872 till his death, at Petrograd, on February 28, 1887.

He had dabbled in music from childhood: he recognized his amateurishness after his meeting with Bala-kireff, with whom he made serious studies in technique. His output, for a man who could practise music only in the rare intervals of freedom from quite other professional work, was pretty considerable. His works include an opera *Prince Igor* (left unfinished, but completed by Rimsky-Korsakoff and Glazounoff), two symphonies, a Symphonic Sketch *In the Steppes of Central Asia*, two string quartets, two movements of an unfinished symphony, an unfinished opera-ballet *Mlada*, about a dozen songs, a few piano pieces, etc.

CUI, CÉSAR ANTONOVITCH

Born at Vilna, January 18, 1835. His mother was a Lithuanian, his father a French officer wounded in Napoleon's Russian campaign of 1812 and left behind in the retreat. He studied music at an early age, and in 1849 had some lessons from the Polish composer Moniuzsko. In 1850 he entered the Petrograd School of Military Engineering, where he remained for seven years; at the end of his studentship he became a sub-professor in the School. He afterwards had a distinguished career as a lecturer on fortifications and kindred subjects. Among his pupils were General Skobeleff and the late Czar Nicholas II.

He kept up his music during his engineering studies; and the turning-point in his career as a musician came when he made the acquaintance of Balakireff in 1856. It was under the latter's stimulus that he began to compose. He became one of the " Five," and did a great deal of journalistic work for the nationalistic school — incidentally making a number of enemies for it and for himself. He died in 1918.

He wrote some hundred and thirty songs, a quantity of choral and piano music, eight operas — *The Mandarin's Son* (1859), *The Prisoner of the Caucasus* (1859), *William Ratcliff* (1869), *Angelo* (1876), *The Saracen*, (1889), *The Filibusterer* (1894), *A Feast in Plague-Time*, and *Mam'zelle Fifi* (1903), several works for violin, string quartet, etc., and several for orchestra, of which perhaps the best known is the suite *In Modo Populari*. His book on *Music in Russia* did a great deal to interest Western Europe in Russian music.

DARGOMIJSKY, ALEXANDER SERGEI-VITCH

Born in the Government of Toula, February 14, 1813, of well-to-do parents. He received an amateurish musical education as a boy, and began composing at fifteen. In 1831 he entered the Government service, but retired four years later, having kept up his musical studies meanwhile. He met Glinka in 1833, who urged him to a more rigorous study of theory and technique. In 1839 he wrote his first opera *Esmeralda*, which was not produced, however, until 1847 (at Moscow). His next big work, *The Triumph of Bacchus*, was first designed as a cantata (1842), then transformed into an opera ballet (1848). *The Roussalka* followed in 1856. He travelled abroad in 1864, and on his return to Russia joined Balakireff and his friends in the movement for the making of a national school of music. His last opera, *The Stone Guest*, in which he carried out to the full his doctrine of a vocal line that should be part melody, part recitative, was left unfinished at his death in January, 1869, and was completed by Cui and Rimsky-Korsakoff, and produced in February, 1872.

His other works include a few pieces for orchestra (*Kazachok*, *Baba-Yaga*, *The Dance of Mummers*, etc.), and for piano, and many songs, vocal duets, trios, quartets, and choruses.

GLIÈRE, REINHOLD MORISSOVITCH

Born at Kief, January 11, 1875. Studied at the Moscow Conservatoire, under Taneieff, Ippolitoff-Ivanoff, and Hrjimaly (violin), from 1894 to 1900. In 1914 he became director of the Kief Conservatoire. His largest works are three symphonies and a symphonic poem *The Sirens*. The others include two string quartets and other chamber music works, pieces for piano and various other instruments, and a large number of songs.

GLINKA, MICHAIL IVANOVITCH

Born at Novospasskoi, in the Government of Smolensk, June 2, 1804, of rich parents. He received a smattering of musical education at home in childhood, and absorbed many impressions from the folk music of the neighborhood. He was at school in Petrograd from 1817 to 1822, during which time he had a few piano lessons from Field. He took up the violin also, and dabbled in composition without having had any proper technical training. After a period of travel, he settled in Petrograd in 1824, in a government office, took up singing, and continued to compose like an amateur. He resigned his office in 1828, and travelled extensively in Europe during the next few years. In 1833, in Berlin, he went through a systematic study of harmony, counterpoint, and composition, under Dehn.

He returned to Russia in 1834, possessed with the idea of writing a Russian national opera. This was realized in *A Life for the Czar*, which was first performed on November 27, 1836, with immediate success. From 1836 to 1839 he acted as choirmaster in the Imperial Chapel. His second opera, *Rousslan and Ludmilla*, was given in November, 1842. Its cold reception depressed him, and he went abroad again in 1844, travelling principally in France and Spain. In Paris, under the influence of Berlioz, he conceived the ambition of becoming an orchestral composer: his chief works in this line were the *Jota Aragonesa*, the *Night in Madrid*, and the *Kamarinskaya*, all written between 1848 and 1852. He returned, after many wanderings and home-comings, to Petrograd, when the Crimean War broke out in 1854. He visited Berlin again in 1856, and died there on February 3, 1857.

Besides the works above mentioned, he wrote a string quartet, a sextet for piano and strings, a trio for piano, clarinet, and bassoon, and other chamber music works, many piano pieces, choruses, songs, and duets, the incidental music to Count Koukolnik's tragedy *Prince Kholmsky*, etc.

GRETCHANINOFF, ALEXANDER TICHO-NOVITCH

Born at Moscow, October 13, 1864. He entered the Moscow Conservatoire in 1881, studying under Kashkin, Safonoff (piano), Laroche and Hubert (counterpoint), and Arensky (harmony). Later he took lessons from Taneieff, and entered the Petrograd Conservatoire in 1890, where he worked under Rimsky-Korsakoff. He returned to Moscow in 1896. Here his opera *Dobrinya Nikitich* (begun in 1895) was performed in 1903. His other works include an opera on Maeterlinck's *Sister Beatrice*, two symphonies, a piano trio, a setting of Ostrovsky's *Snow-Maiden*, and many songs.

IPPOLITOFF–IVANOFF, MICHAIL MICHAILOVITCH

(Ippolitoff was his mother's name. He added the prefix because there was another Michail Michailovitch Ivanoff.) Born at Gatschina, November 19, 1859. Was at the Petrograd Conservatoire from 1875 to 1882 under Rimsky-Korsakoff (composition). In the latter year he became director of the Music School, and conductor of the Symphony Concerts of the Imperial Russian Musical Society at Tiflis. In 1884 he became conductor also of the opera there. Settled in Moscow in 1893 as professor of composition at the Conservatoire. Six years later he became conductor of the Moscow Private Opera. He has composed several operas, —*Ruth* (Tiflis, 1887), *Assya* (Moscow, 1900), *The Betrayal* (Moscow, 1911), etc.,—cantatas and other choral works, overtures (*Yar Khmel*, *Spring*, *Medea*), a symphony, the well-known suite *Caucasian Sketches*, a piano quartet, a string quartet, and several songs. He has written books on harmony and on the folksongs of Georgia.

JACOBSON, MYRON

KALINNIKOFF, BASIL SERGEIVITCH

Born January 13, 1866, at Voina, in the Government of Orlov. Educated at the Orlovsky Seminary. In 1884 he entered the Music School of the Moscow Philharmonic Society, studying the bassoon and composition under Ilyinsky and Blaramberg. He left the school in 1892, and in the season 1893–94 acted as second conductor at the Moscow Italian Opera. His health giving way, he had to go to the South. He died of consumption at Jalta, January 11, 1901. He is best known abroad by his first symphony, in G minor. In addition to this he wrote a second symphony, various other orchestral works, a string quartet, a cantata (*St. John Damascene*), overture and incidental music to Tolstoi's play *Czar Boris*, symphonic poems (*The Nymphs* and *Cedar and Palm*), a ballad for soli, chorus, and orchestra (*The Roussalka*), piano pieces, and songs.

KOPYLOFF, ALEXANDER

Born July 14, 1854. Has written a symphony, an overture, an orchestral scherzo, two string quartets, songs, etc.

KORESTSCHENKO, ARSENI NIKOLAIE-VITCH

Born December 18, 1870. Studied at the Moscow Conservatoire under Taneieff and Arensky. From 1891 taught counterpoint and form at the Conservatoire. His works include the operas *Belshazzar's Feast* (1892), *The Angel of Death*, *The Ice Palace* (1900), music to Euripides' *Iphigenia in Aulis* and *The Trojan Women*, the ballet *The Magic Glass* (1902), a *Symphonie Lyrique*, a *Barcarolle*, an *Armenian Suite*, and *Musical Pictures* for orchestra, a Fantasia for piano and orchestra, a cantata (*Don Juan*), a string quartet, songs, pieces for piano, violin, violoncello, etc.

LIAPOUNOFF, SERGEI MICHAILOVITCH

Born at Jaroslav, November 30, 1859. Studied at Nijni-Novgorod, afterwards at the Moscow Conservatoire. He left the latter in 1883. Settled in Petrograd in 1885. In 1893 he embarked on a folksong collecting expedition in the Governments of Vologda, Viatka, and Kostroma; and from 1894 to 1902 acted as assistant director of the Imperial Chapel. His works include an orchestral *Ballade*, an *Overture Solennelle*, a symphony in B minor, two symphonic poems, two piano concertos, an *Ukrainian Rhapsody* for piano and orchestra, many piano pieces (including twelve *Etudes d'exécution transcendente*), several songs, etc. He edited the correspondence between Balakireff and Tchaïkovsky.

MEDTNER, NICOLAI

Born in Moscow, December 24, 1879, of German parents. He entered the Conservatoire there in 1891, studying under Safonoff. He left the Conservatoire in 1900, won the Rubinstein prize for piano-playing, and toured Russia and Germany as a concert pianist; on his return to Moscow he became professor of the piano at the Conservatoire. His works are almost all for the piano: they include three sonatas, a *Sonate-Ballade*, and a *Sonaten-Triade*. In addition he has published a sonata for violin and piano, *Three Nocturnes* for the same combination, and a number of striking songs. During the Great War he wrote a piano concerto, which is not yet published.

MOUSSORGSKY, MODEST PETROVITCH

Born at Karevo, in the Government of Pskov, March 29, 1839. He received a good training in singing and the piano as a boy at home; his studies were continued when, in 1849, he went to Petrograd to attend the Cadets' School, in preparation for a military career. In 1856 he was gazetted to the famous Preobrajensky regiment. In this and the next year he met Dargomijsky, Balakireff, and Borodine, and other members of the new Russian group, and set himself more seriously to the study of music. He left the army in 1861 to devote himself to the art, but he soon had to accept a small government post that hardly sufficed to keep him from utter poverty. After various tentative efforts, he entered the operatic field with *Boris Godounoff* (produced in Petrograd in 1874). This was followed by *Khovantchina*, which was left unfinished at the composer's death, completed and orchestrated by Rimsky-Korsakoff, and first performed in its entirety in 1885. Moussorgsky died in Petrograd, March 28, 1881.

His other works include the unfinished operas *The Matchmaker* (Gogol), *Salammbo* (Flaubert), a few orchestral works (*Intermezzo in modo classico*, a *Scherzo*, a *Turkish March*, and *Night on the Bare Mountain*), and many remarkable songs, the piano pieces *Pictures from an Exhibition*, etc.

MODERN RUSSIAN SONGS
VOLUME I

SPRING

(Original Key, B)

Translated from the Russian
of A FET
by Frederick H. Martens

ACHILLES ALPHERAKY, Op.16, № 1
(1846 -   )

ML-2876-3

2

loam._____ The vales are green with bud-ding

grass_ _es, On ev_ _'ry bush the dew-pearls

glow, Bird-songs ring clear as spring-time pass _ es, The

cloud - chain cracks at light-ning's blow. A -

gain, a - gain my heart - beats time their

meas - ure To sounds that speak of home,_____ As the

blos - soms of spring - tide deck the loam._____

poco mosso e cresc.

cresc.

dim.

dim.

ff

THE BOUQUET

(Composed in 1892)

(Original Key, A)

Translated from the Russian
of VELICHKO (after Hafiz)
by Constance Purdy

ACHILLES ALPHERAKY, Op.16, № 5

(1846 -   )

ML-2875-2

splen - dor They dared to ri - - val you when

hom-age they should ren - der. The cul - - prits

bound to - geth - er At your feet I lay!

WHEN NOCTURNAL SHADOWS GLIDING

THE SONG OF SONGS

(*Original Key, B minor*)

Translated from a Russian paraphrase
of "The Song of Solomon" Chap. III
by Frederick H. Martens

ACHILLES ALPHERAKY, Op. 21, № 1
(1846 -   )

ML-2878-6

Ah, I find him not whose pow - - - er And whose

man - ly strength and beau - ty Fill my ar - dent soul with yearn - ing.

recitando

I sought my love and found him not, and sought a -

gain, I call'd his name un - ceas - ing, yet I call'd in

vain.

From my couch I rose, the cit-y slum-ber-bound and si-lent rest-ing: And by

long-ing torn I wan-der'd, tho' how vain my ut-most quest-ing. Oh, did no one see my lov - er, ____ nor his way dis - cov - er?

Watch - men, has he pass'd your por - tals, the fair - est of all

mor - tals? O'er all the world I've sought him who __ my love did

gain, I've sought him, call'd up - on his name, yet all in vain. __

I will find my love, though in my search The grave a - lone re - quite me; Since no fear nor doubt af - fright me. And once found the pow - er burn - ing Of my kiss his free - dom

WHEN LEAVES ARE FALLING SERE

Translated from the Russian
of A UMANETZ
by Frederick H. Martens

(Original Key, D)

ACHILLES ALPHERAKY, Op. 26, No. 3
(1846-)

flow - ers grow in rich and fra - grant bloom, ___

The flow'rs my heart bade germ - i - nate In ___ all their ra - diant

beau - ty.

Ah, pluck, ___ ah,

pluck those flow - ers grow - ing on my qui - et grave! With

them your dear blonde head a - dorn,_____ be - lov - ed! They are

bear - ing, are bring-ing you the song that fills my soul. They

bear the word - less mes - sage of my love.

To V. P. Damaev
ALL THE BELLS, THE LITTLE BELLS
(Original Key, E minor)

Translated from the Russian
of CKITALTZ by Constance Purdy

M. BAGRINOFSKI

Rapidly, with assurance (♩=120)

VOICE

PIANO

All the

bells, _____ the lit-tle bells are ring-ing clear And a

sim - - - ple tale are tell - ing in their sound.

Swift the troi - ka, snow - lumps fly-ing far and

ML-2881-7

slightly slower (♩ = 104)

Ah! Fly, thou my soul! Sur - ren - - - der thou to dreams. Ban-ish dis-mal fa - ces in ___ the mer - - ry dance.

Singing, tenderly

Eyes be - lov - ed in the dark - ness send their beams. Vel - - vet - black the lash - es out from which they

DEEP HIDDEN IN MY HEART
(IN MEINEM HERZCHEN)

Gr. A. GOLENISTSCHEFF KUTUSOFF
English translation by Constance Purdy
German translation by G. Löwenthal

ANTON ARENSKY, Op. 44, No 6

5-138-71495-4

yet she the thresh-old pass'd,___ And fas - ten'd close the door,___
schlich sie sich heim - lich ein,___ schloss hin - ter sich die Thür___

___ in shel - ter there a - bid - - ing.
___ und weicht___ nicht mehr von hin - - nen.

Since then,___ when-e'er my soul___ is fill'd with doubt and fear___
Seit - dem,___ wenn mein Ge - müth,___ von All tags-sor - gen schwer,___

That by___ their wan-ton sport___ sink hap - pi - ness and rea - - son,
Die eig' - ne Zwei-fel sucht___ kein Glücks-ge - fühl lässt blei - - ben,

in con - so - la - tion bring - ing.____ Once more____
singt mir von Glück und Won - ne.____ Ich fühl'____

____ to joy I wake.... the storm____ clouds roll - ing back, We
____ mich neu - be - lebt, es weicht____ die Sor - ge bang dem

lis - ten to my cap - tive, in the still - ness sing - ing.____
Sang der Zau - be - rin, wie Ne - bel von der Son - ne.____

REVERY
(IM HALBSCHLAF)

Translated from the Russian
of L. MUNSCHTEIN by Constance Purdy
German version by Lina Esbeer

ANTON ARENSKY, Op.60, No.3
(1862-1906)

My eyes are clos-ing in a drows-y, la-zy slum-ber
Die Au-gen schlie-ssen sich vom Schlum-mer leicht ge-trü-bet;

I am con-tent, for thro' the sleep-y haze, I feel that some one loves me
mir ist so wohl des Halb-schlafs Hül-le lässt mich wäh-nen, dass mich Je-mand

tru-ly just a lit-tle, So light-ing with the joy of
ein klein we-nig lie-bet, dass mir der Lenz ver-klärt der

ML-2916-2

spring my au-tumn days.____ And dark and pen-sive eyes are
Herb-stes-ta-ge Rest.____ Wie freund-lich lä-cheln mir die

look-ing at me kind-ly, Sweet words of love I in the eve-ning still-ness reap;
träu-me-ri-schen Bli-cke, manch Lie-bes-wort durch-dringt die a-bend-li-che Ruh.

Un-real tho' these may be as fair-y tales of child-hood,
Und sind es Mär-chen nur von still er-sehn-tem Glü-cke,

I love to hear them while I'm dream-ing half a-sleep.
so hört in hal-bem Traum sich's ih-nen woh-lig zu.

SONG OF THE LITTLE FISH
(FISCHLEINS LIED)

Translated from the Russian
'of M. LERMONTOFF
by Robert H. Hamilton
German version by Lina Esbeer

(Original Key, Bb)

ANTON ARENSKY, Op. 27, Nº 1
(1862-1906)

O stay, _____ my _____
O bleib' bei

child, _____ And lin - ger here by ___ me!
mir, _____ *Mein hol - der Kna - be ___ du!*

Here dwell the wa - ter spir-its
Es lebt sich frei im Was - ser

ML - 2880 - 6

wild, _____
hier; _____
In cool- -ness rests the
So kühl ist's, so voll

sea. _____
Ruh'. _____

My mer - ry sis - ters call thee here, _____
Die Schwe - stern ru - fe ich her - bei, _____
All cir - cling
Wir schwin - gen

in ___ the dance, _____
uns ___ im Tanz, _____
Thy wear - y, care - worn
Bis dei - ne mü - de

life _____ to me. _____ O
Wel - ____ - len - meer. _____ Mein

treas - _____ - ure mine, ____ O treas - _____ - ure
trau - _____ - ter Schatz, ____ mein trau - _____ - ter

mine, _____ O tar - ry here with me! _____
Schatz, _____ o blei - be hier bei mir! _____

THE EAGLE
(DER ADLER)
(Original Key)

Translated from the Russian
of Count GOLENISTSCHEFF-KUTUSOFF
by Frederick H. Martens
German version by G. Löwenthal

ANTON ARENSKY, Op. 44, № 1
(1862-1906)

An ea-gle poised on crag-gy
Ein Ad-ler sass auf Fels-ge-

peak, His vis-ion lost in space sur-round-ing,___ Like
stein, den Blick ge-rich-tet in die Wei-te,___ dem

pil-grim lone, whose mind a-far___ The un-known deeps of thought is
Pil-ger gleich, der ganz al-lein___ tief-ern-stem Sin-nen wird zur

ML-2879-6

He scorns the birds' dis - cor - dant cries,   The whirl-wind's
Doch schien er nicht die Vo - gel schaar,   noch auch den

fu - rious rage dis - dain - ing,____ A - loof,   the mas-ter óf the
Wir - bel - wind zu hö - ren,____ es liess der kö - nig - li - che

skies____ Still holds the dream past their at - tain - ;ing.
Aar____ in sei - nem Sin - nen sich nicht stö - ren.

E - nough of dream-ing! But a glance   At earth's poor
Ge - nug des Sin - nens! Ei - nen Blick   des Er - den-

ML - 2879 - 6

light, His up-ward flight leaves far be - hind him, No
tand hat bald er hin - ter sich ge - las - sen, und

chains of hate or love may bind him, In az-ure
un - be-rührt von Lieb' und Has - sen, im blau-en

deeps he fades from sight.
Ae - ther er ent - schwand.

BURNING OUT IS THE SUNSET'S RED FLAME

(Original Key)

Translated from the
Russian of V. KULCHINSKY
by Constance Purdy

MILI BALAKIREFF
(1837-1910)

Burn-ing out is the sun-set's red flame,_____ Gold-en moun - tains are deep-'ning to shad - ow; Tran-quil eve - ning puts

ML-2882-4

forth now her claim, _____ Si-lence falls o - ver

for - - est and mead - ow.

p

O for - get _____ thou, my heart, all those days, _____ Days re -

bel - lious, in-spired and soul-free-ing.   My poor heart, seek the sleep which al-lays!

My poor heart, seek the sleep which al-lays!

Call not back.___ those dear hours in - to be - ing!

From the clouds comes the moon's gen-tle light,

Sil-ver

flood- -ed the fields soft-ly glit - ter, Why, O

why_____ can she not by her might Heal the

wounds of my soul, deep and bit - ter?_____

THE PINE-TREE
(DER FICHTENBAUM)

(*Original Key, F♯ minor*)

Translated from the Russian
of LERMONTOFF by Constance Purdy
German version by Lina Esbeer

MILI BALAKIREFF
(1837-1910)

By snow-fields en-com-pass'd a-lóne stands a pine-tree In
Auf ein-sa-mer Hö-he er-starrt und ver-las-sen Im

cold north-ern win-ter and night: And slow-ly and soft-ly in
Nor-den ein Fich-ten-baum steht: Er wiegt sich im Schlum-mer von

slum-ber is sway-ing, All clad in a gar-ment of white.
schim-mern-den Mas-sen Des Schnees wie von Lin-nen um-weht.

ML-2884-2

NOCTURNE
(NACHTSTÜCK)
(Original Key, D)

Translated from the Russian
by Frederick H. Martens

MILI BALAKIREFF
(1837-1910)

VOICE

PIANO

How clear were the skies the night that is gone, How
Wie war sie so klar die ges-tri-ge Nacht, Wie

count-less the stars whose ra-diance the dawn Did cap-ture!
hat-te sie all' die Stern-lein ent-facht So son-nig!

A dream 'neath the heav'ns the wide mead-ows lay, The
Beim Blick auf die Hö-hen den schlum-mern-den Hain, Die

calm lake re-flect-ing the stars' sil-ver ray; I thought then: ah,
Wäs-ser, hell schim-mernd im himm-li-schen Schein, Da dacht' ich: stets

ML-2883-5

might this fair mo - ment stay— What rap -ture! The
von euch um-ge-ben zu sein— Wie won-nig! Wie

Listesso tempo

wave, ah, how fair and the steppe how— wide, How
schön ist die Wo - ge die Step - pe so weit, Wie

charm - ing the Spring in the dress of a bride, We're— find - ing; How
schön in des Len - zes bunt schim-mern - den Kleid Die— Blu - me; Wie

poco a poco agitato e cresc.

ra - diant, ex - alt - ed, is love's glow - ing light, How
hehr ist der Lie - be hell glän - zen - des Licht, Wie

poco a poco agitato e cresc.

49

earth has no joy such as that up yon - der!
bes ser wohl ist es als hier Da dro - ben!

No joy like
Bes - ser ist

that up yon - der! _____
es da dro - ben!

THE FAIR GARDEN

ROMANCE

(Original Key)

Translated from the Russian
by Constance Purdy

ALEXANDER BORODINE
(1834-1887)

ML-2885-3

To Modest P. Moussorgsky

A DISSONANCE

ROMANCE

(*Original Key, Db*)

English version by
FREDERICK H. MARTENS

ALEXANDER BORODINE
(1834-1887)

ML-2918-2

while A dis - so - nance, you re - veal it In

voice and in glance, and in smile! You know, nor may you con -

ceal it!

MY SONGS ARE ENVENOMED AND BITTER
(MON CHANT EST AMER ET SAUVAGE)

(Original Key)

French version (after HEINE)
by Paul Collin
English version by Charles Fonteyn Manncy

ALEXANDER BORODINE
(1834-1887)

The composer used a free metrical version in Russian of Heine's poem, which makes the retention of the German original impossible.

Copyright MCMXIX by Oliver Ditson Company

M L - 2886 -2

My songs are en - ven - om'd and bit - ter, Yet how could they oth-er-wise
Mon chant est a - mer et sau - va - ge, com - ment pour - rait - il ê - tre

be? A ser - pent I bear in my heart, In the heart that is
doux? Je porte un ser - pent dans mon soeur, dans ce coeur que rem -

fill'd, love, with thee.
plit ton a - mour.

THE SEA
(LA MER)

Translated by Grace Hall
French version by Paul Collin

(Original Key, G♯ minor)

ALEXANDER BORODINE

Allegro tempestuoso
sempre legato

The sea toss - es and raves, While fling - ing heav'n - - ward its

La mer gronde et mu - git, rou - lant ses flots en fu -

ML-2993-12

heart is at peace, full of joy and of won-der, For love soon will crown hap-py
tout es-pé-rer l'a-ve-nir le con-vi-e, l'a-mour ra-di-eux va bril

days with-out num - ber.
ler sur sa vi - e.

Tempo I

The sea
La mer

toss - es and raves,_____
gronde et mu - git,_____

While fling - ing
rou - lant ses

heav'n - ward its waves.
flots en fu - rie,

Stead-fast-ly steer-ing the ma-ri-ner
fier et vail-lant le ma-rin veut aux

stands by the rud - der;
flots te - nir tê - te.
With
Il

cour - age un - fail - ing he smiles where one wis - er might
lutte, il com - bat, il s'a - charne à dom - pter la tem -

shud - der.
pê - te.
The
La

bil - - lows shout ven - - geance, they laugh in his
vague è - *cu* - *meu* - - *se* *lui* *crache* *au* *vi* -

face; With death for op -
sa - *ge,* *il* *pous* - *se* *la*

po - - nent how win the race?
bar - - *que* *loin* *du* *ri* - *va* - *ge.*

Till, _____ toss'd at ran - - - dom, the
_Et_ _____ _bal - lot - té - - - e au_

sport _____ of the **blast** _____
gré _____ _de la mer_ _____

A - **gainst** _____ the rocks he
la bar - - - que som - - bre

dash - **es** at **last.** _____
_au_ _gouffre_ _a_ _mer._ _____

To Nickolas Rimsky-Korsakoff

THE SLEEPING PRINCESS
(LA PRINCESSE ENDORMIE)
BALLADE

Translated from the Russian
by Constance Purdy
French version by Grandmousin

Words and Music by
ALEXANDER BORODINE
(1834 - 1887)

With - -in the for - est deep Lies the prin - cess
Dans le bois té - né - breux La prin - cesse aux

fast a - sleep: Veil'd by night and dark - ness som - bre,
si doux yeux, Par le char - me d'u - ne fé - e,

She, with eye - lids seal'd in slum - ber, Sleeps,
Au som - meil est con - dam - née, Et dort!

ML-2887-6

sleeps!
dort!

Più mosso

All at once the for-est qui-et Wakes to laugh-ter wild and ri-ot;
Mais sou-dain dans l'ombre é-paisse é-cla-tent des cris et des ri-res;

Witch-es, sat-yrs nois-y swarm Round the maid-en's sleep-ing form.
les es-prits des bois pas-sent en ron-de sans rom-pre ce som-meil.

Tempo I

Ev - er, in the for - est deep, That en - chant - ed, death - like sleep
Sans cou - leur, com - me la mort, La prin - ces - se tou - jours dort!

She sleeps!
dort! dort!

Più animato

Le - gends say that to her bow - er There will come a prince, whose pow - er
On di - sait qu'en la fo - rêt un jour vien - drait un preux, un che - va -

ML-2887-6

one the days are go - ing, In - to years and cy - cles
jours s'en vont sans trè - ve, *Le temps pas - se comme un*

grow - ing; Still there comes of life no sound; All is
rê - ve, *Et ja - mais nul n'ap - pa - raît* *Dans la*

Tempo I

wrapt in sleep pro - found! So with - in the
nuit de la fo - rêt! *La prin - cesse aux*

for - est deep Lies the prin - cess fast a - sleep.
si doux yeux, *Au re - pos mys - té - ri - eux,*

Seal'd her eyes in ma - gic slum - ber, She, thro' days that
Par le char - me d'u - ne fé - e Au som - meil est

none can num - ber, Sleeps, sleeps!
con - dam - née, Et dort! dort!

And no liv - ing soul can tell When she'll wa - ken from the
Quel fa - tal et mor - ne som - meil! Quand son - ne - ra l'heu - re du ré-

spell.
veil?

WHEN GAZING IN THINE EYES
(WENN ICH IN DEINE AUGEN SEH')

HEINRICH HEINE *) (1799-1856)
Translated by Arthur Westbrook

(Original Key, E)

J. BLEICHMANN, Op. 8, No. 4

*) The music was composed to a Russian version of Heine's poem.

ML-3003-2

dream of heav'n could be more blest:_____
ü - ber mich wie Him - mels - lust;_____

pp *quasi parlando*

But when thou say'st: "I love but theel"
doch wenn du sprichst: ich lie - be dich!

I fall to weep - ing,
so muss ich wei - nen,

weep - ing bit - ter - ly._____
wei - nen bit - ter - lich._____

col canto

a tempo

morendo

AH, IF MOTHER VOLGA
(ACH, WENN MUTTER WOLGA)

(Original Key, A minor)

Translated from the Russian
of Count A. TOLSTOI by Constance Purdy
German version by Lina Esbeer

CÉSAR CUI, Op. 67
(1835-1918)

Ah, if Moth-er Vol-ga could turn back in her flow-ing!
Ach, wenn Mut-ter Wol-ga doch auch rück-wärts möcht' rin-nen!

If we might our lives live o'er a-gain, know-ing!
Ach, könnt' man das Le - ben von Neu-em be - gin - nen!

Ah, if flow'rs in win-ter could fra-grance keep send-ing! And could but one love be
Thä-ten sich im Win-ter gar Blu-men ent-fal-ten! Woll-ten wir uns lie - ben

ML-2888-4

faith-ful and un-end-ing! / If the o-cean's depths we, my
und auch Treu-e hal-ten! / *Könn-ten wir die Tie-fen des*

broth-ers, could meas-ure! / If a maid-en's beau-ty
Mee-res er-schau-en / *und den sü-ssen Re-den*

trust as well as treas--ure! /
schö-ner Mäd-chen trau--en!

Ah, could each old wife be youth-ful as her daugh - ter!
Ach, wenn al - le Wei - ber jun - ge Weib - lein wä - ren!

If were in the wine - flask a lit - tle less wa - ter!
Man sein Fläsch-chen Brannt - wein ver - dünnt nicht müsst' lee - ren!

If to seek our lips were but the gob-let's mis - sion!
Wenn der vol - le Be - cher ständ' den Lip-pen nä - her.

Could the dev-il take all ty - rants to per - di - tion!
Wenn der Teu - fel hol - te al - le Rechts - ver - dre - her!

To Valentine Constantinovna Liadoff

DUSK FALLEN

Translated from the Russian
by Constance Purdy

CÉSAR CUI
(1835 -   )

ML-2889-2

Thy smile was as of yore, I loved it, oh how dear - ly, Thy soft - ly wov - en braids held

once a-gain their pow'r; Thy som-bre eyes re-flect-ing all their old-time sad - ness,

Look'd in - to mine once more at eve - ning's qui - et hour, at

eve - ning's qui - et hour.

HUNGER SONG
(DAS HUNGERLIED)

(Original Key, A minor)

Translated from the Russian
of N. NEKRASOFF
by Deems Taylor

CÉSAR CUI
(1835-1918)

ML-2890-3

His ash - en face is gaunt and worn; How glazed and dim his fail - ing eyes.
Er selbst ist fahl, sein Blick ist leer, als ob er stets im Rau - sche wär'.

He walks, he crawls, He moans, he sighs. And now be - hold the rus-tling
Er geht im Schlaf, er keucht, und kriecht da - hin wo sich sein Rog-gen

corn! He stops and stares with hun - gry eyes, He sways,
wiegt. Dort steht er wie ein Göt - zen-bild und singt

and fall - ing faint - ly cries: "O corn,____ put forth____
kein Laut der Brust ent-quillt: „Ge - deih',____ ge - deih'____

ML-2890-3

O THOU ROSE-MAIDEN

(Original Key, A minor)

**Translated from the Russian
of A. PUSHKIN**
by Constance Purdy

ALEXANDER DARGOMIJSKY
(1813-1869)

ML-2891-4

The night-in-gale— with-in the lau- -rel,

Of wood-land song- -sters— feath- -er'd king,

Near that proud— flow- -er of rare— beau- -ty,

The rose so haugh- -ty of rare beau- -ty,

slowly dim.

In sweet-est thrall-dom spends his days, In sweet - est

thrall - dom spends _____ his days,

And soft - - ly sings _____ to ___

her his ___ lays, And soft - - ly sings _____

to her his lays,   And soft - - -

- - -ly   sings _____ to

her, and soft - - -ly to _____ her sings _____

his   lays! _____

AH, TWINE NO BLOSSOMS
(O, WINDE KEINE DUFT'GE BLÜTE)

Translated from the Russian
of D. RATHAUS by Deems Taylor
German version by Lina Esbeer

(Original Key, F minor)

REINHOLD GLIÈRE, Op. 18, Nº 7
(1875-)

ML-2892-4

go. _____
ganz. _____

dim.

mf

mf

Ah, come no more to smile up - on me... That
O, dass ich nie dein Lä - cheln schau - te, nie

lim - pid smile so long for - got, _____ My heart's _____ de -
hör - te was dein Mund ver - spricht, _____ mein zar - - tes

p

p

sire, my own be - lov - - ed... Dost thou not hear? _____
Kind, du hol - de Trau - - te, dich wie - der lie - -

cresc.

f

f

ML-2892-4

I love thee not!
-ben will ich nicht!

Oh, wake no more the fire that
Be - sieg des Her - zens heiss Be -

sleep - eth; From pas - sion's bon-dage set me free.
geh - ren, lass mei - ne Ru - he un - ge - stört.

*) English text only.

THE JOURNEY

(Composed in 1840)

(Original Key)

English version by Constance Purdy

MICHAIL IVANOVITCH GLINKA
(1804-1857)

Smoke is ris-ing as the steam-er churns its way, Change, ex-cite-ment un-a-bat-ing, fun, im-pa-tience, ea-ger wait-ing! Crowds of peo-ple all on pleas-ure bent are gay, Fast and fast-er ev-er

ML-3015-7

rid-ing goes the train thro' mead-ows glid - ing; Smoke is ris-ing as the

steam - er churns its way! Change, ex - cite-ment un-a - bat-ing, fun, im-

pa-tience, ea-ger wait-ing, Crowds of peo-ple all on pleas-ure bent are gay,

Crowds of peo-ple all on pleas-ure bent are gay: Fast and

con grazia ed espressione ma leggiero

ing.

1. Yet swift - er by
2. But sun - shine and

p staccato il basso

far do our thoughts__ se - cret fly,___ The heart keep-ing
ver - dure ne'er suf - f'ring re - call;___ And yon - der clear

count as the mo - ments go by; Their deep sub-tle
nights cast their flame o - ver all; Each mo - ment of

gleam on the way__ far ex - tend - ing; You mur - mur: "The
meet - ing with bliss__ o - ver - flow - ing; On hours, e'en of

ML - 3015 - 7

D.C.

time   oft,__ O__ Lord,   seems   un - end - ing!"
part -   - ing,__ hope's sweet   ness   be - stow - ing.

Tempo I

Smoke is   ris - ing as the   steam - er churns its   way! Change, ex -

cite - ment un - a - bat - ing, fun, im - pa - tience, ea - ger wait - ing: Crowds of

peo - ple all on   pleas - ure bent are   gay,   Fast and   fast - er   ev - er rid-ing goes the train thro' mead-ows glid-ing. Smoke is ris-ing as the

steam-er churns its way! Change, ex-cite-ment un-a-bat-ing, fun, im-

pa-tience, ea-ger wait-ing! Crowds of peo-ple all on pleas-ure bent are

gay, Crowds of peo-ple all on pleas-ure bent are gay.

ML-3015-7

STAR OF THE NORTH

(Original Key, D)

Translated from the Russian
of ROSTOPCHINE by Constance Purdy

MICHAIL IVANOVITCH GLINKA
(1804-1857)

'Neath a mar - -vel - lous roof many man - - sions a - rise, But far bright - er than all does one man - - sion stand

ML - 2996 - 4

forth; For a bride dwells there - in, fair-est, sweet - - est of _

all, Of all stars most re-splen - dent, the star_____ of _ the

north. Deep ab - sorb'd doth she brood and sad her thoughts, _ On the

cir - clet of gold, her wed-ding-ring, Great tears from her

eyes— hot and heav-y fall! Of her dear one

is she think-ing night and day.

He, her

hus-band, has gone to a far dis-tant land, And to

her may not soon, may not soon____ come a-gain. He will

come back a-gain when the spring - time shall reign, With God's

sun - -light on high then shall joy____ hold sway.

ON THE STEPPE
(TRISTE EST LE STEPPE)

(Original Key, B minor)

Translated from the Russian
of PLESTCHEIEFF by Charles Fonteyn Manney
French version by M. D. Calvocoressi

ALEXANDER GRETCHANINOFF, Op. 5, № 1
(1864-)

ML-2999-4

Never a flow'r smiles to glad-den me,
Point d'ar-bres verts ni de frais buis-sons

Nev-er a bird sings its
pour a-bri-ter les oi-

lay.
seaux.

Down drops the night on its sa-ble wing,
Lu - gu-bre-ment tombe un soir obs-cur,

Hid-ing each glim-mer-ing star:
pas une é-toile au ciel noir:

What sum-mons back to my
Je ne sais plus quels doux

mem-o-ry
mots d'a-mour,

Vis-ions of you from a-
par un tel soir tu m'as

sempre p

lugubre

mf

p

mf

poco stringendo

poco stringendo e cresc.

Now hear the song of the night-in-gale
les chants su-a-ves des ros-si-gnols

Thrill-ing the spa-ces on
mon-tent des bois par-fu-

high;
més;

Flow'rs in the des-ert are
au-tour de moi mil-le

blos-som-ing,
fleurs sont nées

Stars deck with jew-els the
et tout le ciel re-splen-

sky! _____
dit. _____

PALM BRANCHES

(Original Key)

Translated from the Russian
of A. BLOCK by Grace Hall

ALEXANDER GRETCHANINOFF, Op. 47, N.º 2

(1864-   )

ML-3002-2

way. Lust - y winds blow o'er the sky, Down the rain drops

from on high, Still the flames burn on.

On this Feast of Palms To our Lord we sing our

Psalms From the ear - ly break of dawn.

SLUMBER REIGNS
(ALLES SCHLÄFT)

(Original Key, D)

Translated from the Russian
of A. FET by Frederick H. Martens
German version by S. König

ALEXANDER GRETCHANINOFF
(1864-)

Slum- -ber reigns; Ah, to the gar-den let us go! Slum- ber reigns; The stars a-lone a-bove us glow. Yet the boughs their cu-rious glan-ces from us veil,

Al- -les schläft; Komm', lass uns in den Gar- ten geh'n. Al- les schläft; Nur Ster-ne auf uns nie - der seh'n. Doch sie seh'n uns nicht un - ter den Zwei-gen all';

ML-2895-4

soft - ly stirs and glows: Then re - spond - ing
lei - se bebt und glüht; *Wenn* *dies Be - - ben*

to this si - lent sign of grace, _____ Ar - dent,
nun *bis hin zum Her - zen* *steigt* _____ *Lie - be -*

fond, _____ we are en - clasp'd in love's em - brace! _____
voll _____ *sich Schul - ter* *dann zu Schul - ter neigt.* _____

SNOWFLAKES
(SCHEEFLÖCKCHEN)
(Original Key)

Translated from the Russian
of W. BRÜSSOFF by Constance Purdy
German version by Lina Esbeer

ALEXANDER GRETCHANINOFF, Op. 47, No 1
(1864 -   )

M L-2896-4

you come dan - - - cing. _____
ab vom Him - - - mel. _____

How can we with - stand you long - er! You are
Ge - gen euch sind wir die Schwa - chen,

free, in num - bers strong - er, At your will you can en -
Flöck - chen, ihr könnt la - chen, könnt uns all' zu - sam - men

fold _____ us
fe - - - gen,

In your shroud of white and hold
Stadt und Land ins Bahr - tuch le -

us.
gen.

Snow-flakes fly - ing
We - het, weht ihr

o'er our por-tals, Pit - y us poor mor - tals!
Flo-cken-ster - ne, uns nur bleibt hübsch fer - ne!

ML-2896-4

O you hosts of white ad - van - cing, Out of heav - en
Schnee - ge - stö - ber, Schnee - ge - wim - mel, streut uns Gott her -

you come dan - - - cing.
ab vom Him - - - mel.

cing.
mel.

To J. A. Melinkoff

THE CAPTIVE
(LE CAPTIF)

(Original Key, E)

Translated from the Russian
of **PUSCHKIN** by Grace Hall
French version by M.D. Calvocoressi

ALEXANDER GRETCHANINOFF, Op. 20, №4
(1864-)

ML-2994-4

ANOTHER LITTLE HOUR I BEGGED
(ICH WOLLT' EIN WENIG MIT DIR PLAUDERN)

Translated from the Russian
of A. PLESCHTSCHEJEFF by Constance Purdy
German version by S. König

(Original Key, F)

ALEXANDER GRETCHANINOFF
(1864 -   )

Allegretto

VOICE

PIANO

mf

ben declamando

An-oth-er lit-tle hour I begg'd you To let me lin-ger at your
Ich wollt' ein we-nig mit dir plau-dern, ein Stünd-chen nur mit dir al -

side, But this you ha-sten'd to de-ny me: "I am too bu-sy," you re-
lein; doch du ent-schlüpf-test mir und sag-test: „Ich hab' nicht Zeit, es kann nicht

plied. Then when I told you I was suf-f'ring, And knew no joy with you not
sein." Ich sag-te dir dass ich sehr lei-de, dass all' mein Glück in dei-ner

rit.

ML - 2893 - 3

near,___ You dropp'd a deep, af-fect-ed curt-sey, And out your
Macht,___ doch du ver - beug - test dich nur höh - nisch und ich ward

laugh - - - ter rip-pled clear. To
nichts _____ als aus - ge - lacht. Und

make my heart's pain e-ven great-er, Up to the last your tem-per
um mich dann noch mehr zu quä - len ver-bliebst du trot - zig bis zum

held,___ And, as I would not beg for-give-ness, Your kiss at
Schluss; Trotz al-lem Bit - ten, al - lem Fle - hen Ward zur Ver -

fair!
irrt!

ML-2893-3

THE SIREN
(SIRENE)

Translated from the Russian
of BALMONT
by Frederick H. Martens
German version by S. König

(Original Key, F♯)

ALEXANDER GRETCHANINOFF
(1864 -   )

ML-2984-5

fond pas-sion braves, With such eyes the Si - ren the
Arg - list be - wegt, mit Au - gen gleich die - sen be -

cresc.

heart_____ e'er_____ en - chant_____
stricht_____ die_____ Si - re - - - -

f

p

rit.

- - - - - eth.
- - - - ne.

And
Und

ff rit.

p leggiero

soft_____ and low sound - eth, and ten - der_____ the voice That
mit_____ ih - rer Stim - me, so sanft und_____ so weich ver -

ML-2984-5

lur - eth the sea - man, o'er wild wa - ters tak - en.
lockt sie den Schif - fer im Wel - len - ge - trie - be;

'Tis your ver - y own, and it seems to re - joice
wie ist die - se Stim - me der die - nen doch gleich,

With mirth pure___ and child - like, with love's long - ing shak - en!
bald un - schulds - voll kind - lich, bald zit - ternd___ vor Lie - be.

And
Und

e'er   when his bark   strikes and   staves   on the
wenn   dann sein Fahr - zeug   am   Fel -   sen zer-

rocks   That   ma - gic   song,   drown - ing,   The
schellt,   um - schmei - cheln den   Sin - ken - den

sail - or   en - chant - eth,   And laugh - ter se -
lo - cken - de   Tö - ne,   ver - füh - re - risch'

duc -   tive his   a - go - ny   mocks,
La - chen in's   Ohr   ihm dann   gellt,

FAR ON THE ROAD WE TWO JOURNEYED TOGETHER

(Original Key)

Translated from the Russian
of D. U. TSERTELEV
by Constance Purdy

M. IPPOLITOFF-IVANOFF, Op. 44, № 5

ML-2897-4

once more would say them: Our ways are di-vid-ed and bro-ken the spell.

How can I? How can I? But one word a-lone now is

left me, But one word is left me, and that is of

all words the sad - dest, of all words the sad - dest: Fare-

well! Fare - well! Fare - well!

ONCE THERE LIVED A KING
(ALSATIAN BALLAD)

Translated from the Russian
by Constance Purdy

(Original Key)

M. IPPOLITOFF-IVANOFF, Op. 15, № 3

Once there lived a King, both

old and poor was he, One daugh-ter left of all his treas-ures vast ac-

crued— fair Ger-trude. Near them dwelt young Har-old, a

ML-2946-4

no - ble knight and val - iant, Who scorn - ing oth - er maids and pleas-ures

loved and wooed sweet Ger - trude. All their hopes proved

dross and, a - las! they loved in vain. Fight - ing for the

Cross the knight by Sar - a-cens was slain And she from that day forth doth yearn for his re - turn to Ger - trude.

Day and night thro' dark and light, and in and out of sea - son,__ Ev - er doth she

wait, and grief has robb'd her of her rea - son. And she from that day forth__

doth yearn for his re - turn to Ger - trude.

Once there lived a King, both old and poor was he, One daugh-ter left of all his treas-ure vast ac-crued— fair Ger-trude. So in my coun-try runs the song.

ROMANCE

(Original Key, E)

Original Russian text translated
from the Spanish by V. Botkine
English version by Constance Purdy

M. IPPOLITOFF-IVANOFF
Op.23, Nº 3

O'er peaks of__ the Sier-ra Ne - va - da   Her veil-ing of

haze night   is   fling-ing;   The heat of__ the day has de - part-ed,

ML-2898-4

And com-fort cool breez-es are bring-ing. Let now thy smile en-

chant-ing, My spir-it's fe-ver a-bat-ing, Shine down on me, Zo-

rai-ya, Come at my call, thy lov-er is

wait-ing, Come forth, my be-lov-ed, my fair Zo-rai - ya! Here I lan - guish____ fill'd with long- - ing.____

____ To lands where the palm-trees are grow-ing, With thee would I fly far a-

way, Where on her own shore bloom-ing lone - ly The lo - tus-flow'r

gen - tly doth sway. In our tent we will rest, While the

sun's rays are burn - ing. Come then, come then, Zo - rai - ya,

For thee, my love, thy lov - er is yearn - ing. Come

forth, my be - lov - ed, My fair Zo - rai - ya, Here I

lan - guish fill'd with long - ing!

YOU BROUGHT ME FLOWERS

(Original Key, F♯ minor)

Translated from the Russian
of LOUKIANOFF by Deems Taylor

MYRON JACOBSON, Op. 2, Nº 3

You brought me flow'rs, the fair - est and the last___ I bent my head, and crush'd them with my kiss - es; Your kiss - es

ML - 2899 - 3

too, there on the pet - als lay. And now we two re-call the

past with long - - ing.

Oh, bit - ter hour! Star-ing a -

far you gaze, un-see-ing eyes with si-lent weep-ing blind-ed... Ah,

God of mine! What dreams re-turn, what phan-tom pas-sions rise From these____ pale, dy-ing ro- - - - - - - -ses!

THE LABORER'S PLAINT
(MEDITATION DU LABOUREUR)

Translated from the Russian
of KOLTSOFF by Grace Hall

French version by Mme. Alexandroff

(*Original Key, E minor*)

A. KOPYLOFF

ML - 2947 - 3

friend - ly hand Lifts my heav - y load.
seul a - mi, Pour me se - cou - rir.
Nei - ther goods nor gold,
Point de piè - ces d'or

Nei - ther hearth nor cot,
Gars sans feu ni lieu,
Faith - ful horse or dog
Le che - val te man - que

Soothe my drear - y lot.
Et la herse aus - si.
One lone her - i - tage Did to
J'ai re - çu pour-tant De mon

me be - long, One my fa - ther gave: Man - hood
père un bien, Mon tré - sor u - nique: U - ne

brave and strong. But this bit - ter toil, Hun-ger, need____ and cold, Far from
for - ce mâle Mais le dur____ be - soin De ga - gner____ mon pain Hors de

home____ have made Me un - time - ly old.
mon____ vil - lage A mi - né la for - ce.

Des - o - late, a - lone, In the dark__ I sigh; By sad thoughts be - set, Un - to
Ah, com - ment, mon Dieu, Vivre ain - si__ tout seul? Ce à quoi je songe A ma

Heav'n I cry.
table__ as - sis.

THE SMITH

(Original Key)

Translated from the Russian
by Constance Purdy

A. KORESTSCHENKO, Op. 42, № 3

In my song no gra - ces

lie — that know I!

Nor with

ML-3000-6

sing - ers— may I vie,— Tho' I ri - val smiths de -

fy; I was born a smith to be;— strong— and

free!—

With the forge a - blaze, my

breast____ Holds no words and knows no rest;____

Largamente

To__ my__ song my__ ham - mer__ swings,

For__ a - - way__ it__ sor - row__ flings.____

Sparks in__ air_____ scat - - ter__

care.

p mezza voce   *cresc.*

Thee I   fain would love full   well,___ But in

brawn naught soft   can dwell—   rough___ my___ ways—

Grim is my ca - ress, and   bleak, Words of

love I can-not speak, or___ sweet phrase. Some-thing

says to my__ de- -sire: Stern thy na - ture and se-

vere;___ Ten-der words are not thy sphere. To thy fire!___

Bet - ter far the ham - mer's sound___ With thy

two hands strong and like_____ Hearts of iron with steel bound

round,_____ Strike!_____ Ossia Strike!_____

Ossia

ff

accelerando

cresc.

quanto possibile

sf

STARS ETHEREAL
(KLARE STERNELEIN)

(Original Key, A)

Translated from the Russian
of K. FOFANOFF by Constance Purdy
German version by Lina Esbeer

BASIL KALINNIKOFF
(1866-1901)

ML - 2900- 5

Un poco più vivo

leaf - let with rap - ture thrill'd.
Laub-blaut sich sehnt nach Ruh.

And the dew - la - den
Und die Blu - men be -

blos-soms that ver - y night, Told the tales to the winds that were pass-ing by,
rau - schet vom Thau der Nacht, sie er - zäh - len dem Win - de die Mär-chen schnell,

And__ the mu-ti-nous winds sang them joy-ous-ly O-ver land,
und__ der Wind trägt sie fort, ei - ne leich - te Fracht ü-ber's Land,

o-ver sea, o-ver rock - y height.
ü-ber's Meer, ü-ber's Fels - ge-roll.

rit.

Meno mosso

And the earth 'neath the warmth of spring's ca - ress, In her fair wo-ven
Und die Er - de von Len - zes-lust hoch ge-schwellt pran-get fröh - lich in

Meno mosso

p

garment of green-er-y, Pour'd the tales of the stars and their ten - der-ness
lich-tem Sma-rag-den-glanz, und er-füllt mir mit Mär-chen der Ster - nen-welt

O'er my soul in the thrill of love's ec - sta-sy.
die nach Lie - be sich seh - nen-de See - le ganz.

poco rit.

Tempo I   Con moto

In these days when my
Und zur trau - ri - gen

p

spir-it is sore op-press'd In the dark of these nights drear and sor-row-ful
herbst-li-chen Jah-res-zeit, bin in stür-mi-schen Näch-ten ich ganz al-lein,

espressivo *rit.* *a tempo*

I give back to you, stars clear and beau-ti-ful, All your tales with their
dann er-zähl' ich euch wie-der, ihr Ster-ne-lein, eu-re sin-ni-gen

molto rit. *a tempo*

won-der of depth and rest.
Mär-chen von Freud' und Leid.

NOCTURNE

(Original Key, Db)

Original Russian text by A. CHOMIAKOFF
English version, translated from the French
of M. D. Calvocoressi, by Constance Purdy

S. LIAPOUNOFF, Op. 14, №3,
(1859-)

Moderato

PIANO

Twi-light of eve-ning soft-ly has spread,

The cres-cent moon her star host has led Thro'

space az-ure gleam- -ing:

ML-3009-9

Calm and blest sea - son when love is ful - fill'd,

Earth air and heav - en with ra - di - ance fill'd,

Waves ev - er rest - - - less their

pp

pp mormorendo

8va bassa

8va bassa

tu - - mult have still'd,_____

And o - - - - - cean lies

dream - - ing.

poco rit.

a tempo

Peace - ful my spir - it, land lies re - mote,

As tho' en - chant - - ed slum - bers my boat, Its

droop'd sails in - clin - - ing.

Skies like the o - cean their great vi - gil keep,

Like un - to heav'n blue spar - kles the deep,

Fath - om - less heav'n and

o - cean's wide sweep.

A - like _____ clear and

shin - ing.

O that my

Poco più mosso
a piacere

colla parte

soul might find qui - et and rest!

O that less of - ten were earth - ly her quest On dreams____

____ false de - pend - ing!

rit.

p

Heav'n _____ e - - - ter - - nal re-

flect - - ed might be _____ In beau - - -

ty un - - end - - - ing! _____

CHRISTMAS SONG

(Original Key, B♭)

Translated from the Russian
of A. KORINFSKY by Constance Purdy

S. LIAPOUNOFF, Op. 51, Nº 1

scat - ter'd un-der grow-ing pines, Word doth fol-low word, and bright

poco rit. **Poco più animato**

weave the song in flow-ing lines. Like a check-er'd ta - ble-cloth

spread - ing out al - lur - ing - ly, Spar-kling gold and sil - ver both

thread-ing it en - dur - ing-ly.

Soft the lit - tle car - ol blest sings the praise of home - land fair,

Spins from snow-drops, rasp - ber - ries, cur - rants kiss'd by sun and air,

Far from gar - dens flow'r - ing green swift to o - cean deep it flies,

From blue sea to sea to where flash - ing tur - rets steep a - rise;

ML - 3013 - 5

To her case-ment soar - ing free   thro' all bars that strong im-pede,

Nor of stair   or   path   to guide   doth the wing - ed   song   have need!

Poco meno mosso

Whis-pers to her   heart   laid bare,

floods   its depths with   shin - ing   light.

DEAR LOVE
(LIEB LIEBCHEN)

Russian original from a German text
Translated from the German by Constance Purdy

NICOLAI MEDTNER, Op. 12, Nº 1
(1879-)

ML-2989-3

car-pen-ter grim and spare,___ He's ham-m'ring for___
Zim-mer-mann schlimm und arg,___ *Der zim-mert mir___*

___ me a___ cöf-fin there.___ He knocks and he
___ *ei - nen To-dten - sarg.___* *Es häm - mert und*

ham-mers by day and by night: Long since has he put sleep and rest to flight.___
klop-fet bei Tag und bei Nacht, Es hat mich schon längst um den Schlaf ge-bracht.___

O car-pen-ter, thy work fin-ish fast,____ That soon____
Ach, spu-tet euch, Mei-ster Zim-mer-mann,____ Da-mit

I may____ find sleep____
ich bal-____ -de schla-

at last!
-fen kann!

con strepito

I HAVE COME TO SAY GOOD MORNING

(Original Key)

Translated from the Russian
of A. FETT by George Harris, Jr.

NICOLAI MEDTNER, Op. 24, № 8

M L 2945-4

Gai - ly wak-ing— here a feath-er, There a leaf the breeze is shak - ing,

più dolce

All a-thirst for spring-time weath-er;

poco calando

p poco meno mosso   *cresc.*

And to tell thee how my pas - sion, As last night a -

fresh I met thee,   *mf* Ev - er strives for some new fash - ion

Where - by I can well pro - tect thee;

And to tell how

spring be - sets me, With so sweet a se - cret burn - ing That no words of

mine it lets me Sing

ex - cept with

cresc. e affrettando

3 1 4   1 3 2   3 1 3 2 1 4   5 4 2 3 1

f   *riten.*

its own yearn - - - - - -ing.

riten. poco   *a tempo*

f perdendosi — *p*   *f cantabile*

5   1 4 2 4   ✱ Ped. ✱

accelerando   8

f cantabile   5 3   2 1 5

leggierissimo

8

dim.   *p*

5 3 1 5 2   1

MAY SONG
(MAILIED)

(Original Key, E♭)

JOHANN WOLFGANG von GOETHE
Translated by Constance Purdy

NICOLAI MEDTNER, Op. 6, № 2
(1879 -   )

ML-3005-4

For my sweet — heart was not home; Gold-en Locks the
Fand mein Hold — chen nicht da-heim; muss das Gold- chen

a tempo

poco rit.   p

fields must roam, Green and ra-diant, flow'ring May Draws my dar-ling___ free and
drau-ssen sein; grünt und blü-het___ schön der Mai, Lieb-chen zie-het___ froh und

crescendo   ritenuto   dim.

crescendo   ff

mf

gay.___
frei.___

Tempo I   ten.   ten.

p

Ped.   ※

*) OSSIA
m.d.

On the rocks by the stream, Where that
An dem Fel - sen beim Fluss, wo sie

first kiss su-preme She be-stow'd up-on me, _____ I see some - thing.
reich-te den Kuss, je-nen ers - ten im Gras, _____ seh ich et - - was.

Is _____ it _____ she? _____
Ist _____ sie das? _____

To Fräulein Hedwig Friedrich

SOLITUDE
(EINSAMKEIT)

JOHANN WOLFGANG von GOETHE
Translated by Robert H. Hamilton

NICOLAI MEDTNER, Op. 18, № 3
(1879-)

Ye whose care are the moun-tains and trees,__ O nymphs of the wood-land,
Die ihr Fel-sen und Bäu-me be-wohnt,__ o heil-sa-me Nym-phen,

Grant__ to each in his turn what he in si-lence de-sires.__
Ge-bet jeg-li-chem gern, was er im stil-len be-gehrt,__

Make__ the down-heart-ed one glad,
Schaf-fet dem Trau-ri-gen Trost,

ML- 2991 - 2

FIRST LOSS
(ERSTER VERLUST)

JOHANN WOLFGANG von GOETHE
Translated by Constance Purdy

NICOLAI MEDTNER, Op. 6, № 8
(1879 -   )

ML - 2990 - 3

time _____ of yore! _____
Zeit _____ zu - rück! _____

Lone - ly do __ I nurse my sor - row,
Ein - sam nähr' ich mei - ne Wun - de

And with e'er __ re - new - ing an - guish Mourn for _____ joy that is __ no
und mit stets __ er - neu - ter Kla - ge traur' ich _____ um's ver - lor - ne

more,_____ Ah, who will the days__ so love - ly Of___ that
Glück._____ Ach! Wer bringt die schö - nen Ta - ge, je - ne

hap - py time__ re - store!
hol - de Zeit__ zu - rück!

AH, NOT WITH GOD'S THUNDER

(Original Key, D minor)

Translated from the Russian
of Count A.K. TOLSTOY
by Constance Purdy

MODEST MOUSSORGSKY
(1839-1881)

ML-2901-3

cloud-lets from the heav-ens clear; Then did grim af - flic-tion sow the fin-est rain,

poco cresc.

pp

Sow the fin - est rain of Au-tumn dress, And it sow'd the rain

poco a poco accel.

mf

ver - y long a - go, And it beats and beats un-ceas-ing - ly,

poco a poco accel.

sf *sf* *sf*

cresc. *poco rit.*

Un - ceas-ing-ly, un - tir-ing-ly, end-less-ly it beats, nor stops to rest.

poco rit.

sf *sf* *sf* *sf* *sf*

To Anna Yakovlevna Vorobieff-Petroff

CRADLE SONG

Songs and Dances of Death, № 2

Translated from the Russian
of Count A. Golenistcheff-Koutouzoff
by Constance Purdy

(*Original Key, C minor*)

MODEST MOUSSORGSKY
(1839-1881)

ML-2902-5

Lento *tranquillo*

peace-ful sleep to thy child I am bring-ing: Hush-a-by, by-oh, by-low!

Agitato con dolore

"Pit-y, have pit-y, O Death, cease but a mo-ment Sing-ing thy ter-ri-ble

Lento *tranquillo*

song!" See thou, to rest he's been lull'd by my sing-ing: Hush-a-by, by-oh, by-low!

To César Cui

DARLING SAVISHNA
(SAVICHNA, MA LUMIÈRE)

(Original Key)

Translated from the Russian
of MODEST MOUSSORGSKY by Constance Purdy
French version by J. Sergeunois

MODEST MOUSSORGSKY
(1839-1881)

Voice / Piano

Dar - ling Sa - vish - na,
Bel - le Sa - vich - na,

fal - con bright and pure, Give thy love to me, fool - ish tho' I be,
Oeil de clair fau - con, Sois fi - dèle au fou qui di - vague un peu,

Speak kind words to me in my mis - er - y! O my fal - con dear;
Et ca - res - se - moi de tes longs re - gards! O mon clair fau - con,

ML- 3012 - 5

fal - con bright and pure, Dar-ling Sa-vish-na, sweet I - van-ov-na,
mon fau - con ché - ri, Bel - le Sa-vich-na, mon I - va-nov-na,

From the beg-gar poor do not turn a - way, Drear-y lies my way,
Ne te las-se pas de ton va-nu-pieds, Prends pi - tié de mon

wretch-ed night and day! For the sport of men, look thou, born was I,
sort, de mes tour-ments! Je suis né, vois-tu, vil ho-chet des gens,

For their laugh-ter, ah, yes, to kiss their rod! They call, Sa-vish-na
Pour le ri - re des au - tres, pour leurs jeux! On dit, Sa-vich-na:

me the fool for - lorn, Lis - ten, prais - ing me, "Va - nia, child of God!"
c'est un pau - vre fou. Et l'on m'a nom - mé: Le cé - les - te Jean!

Dar - ling Sa - vish - na, sweet I - van - ov - na, Cuffs and kicks they give
Bel - le Sa - vich - na, chère I - va - nov - na, Le bous - cu - lent - ils,

Va - nia, child of God, With blows hon - or me, nour - ish me with scorn—
Le cé - les - te Jean, Le nous - ris - sent - ils de leurs coups de pied!

But on hol - i - days, all in brave ar - ray, And with rib - bons deck'd,
Mais aux jours de fête où l'on sort pa - ré de ru - bans é - cla-

Speak kind words to me, lost in mis-er-y! Nev-er love like mine
Don - ne - moi ton cœur, à moi qui vais seul! Moi qui t'ai - me comme

has on earth been known, Dar-ling Sa-vish-na, hear me, O my own,
on n'ai - ma ja-mais, O ma Sa-vich-na, qu'on me croie ou non,

Sweet I - van-ov-na!
mon I - va-nov-na!

To Vladimir Vassilevitch Nikolsky

GATHERING MUSHROOMS
(AUX CHAMPIGNONS)
CHANSONNETTE

Translated from the Russian
of L. MEY by Constance Purdy
French version by J.Sergennois

MODEST MOUSSORGSKY
(1839-1881)

ML-2903-4

That for once at least a - ble, They may set a feast ta - ble.
Ser - rent moins la bour - se, les jours où l'on fait la fé - te.

But for thee, thou mean,— hat - ed,
Mais pour toi que j'ab - hor - re,

Wretch-ed do-tard, lean,— sat - ed, Toad-stools I'm ar - ran - ging, that
Vieux, ché - tif et ma - lin - gre, C'est par la fe - nê - tre que

Poi - son - ous, de - cay - ing, at Once for thy a - base - ment, I'll
tou - te la cor - beil - le de cham - pi - gnons pour - ris, ra - bou -

thrust with-in the case - ment, While greed-y he to try of them
gris i - ra trou - ver ton gro-gnon; Poi-son des mou-ches, le

Quick-ly he shall die of them.
vieux é - tran-gle s'il y mord.

But for thee, my pale lov - er,
Ei pour toi, mau - dit hom - me,

I will hill and dale cov - er Till I find a lawn, flow-er'd,
Tê - te blonde au front pâ - le, Je re-cherche une her - be soy -

To Nikolas Rimsky-Korsakoff

HOPAK

Translated from the Russian
of L. MEY by Constance Purdy
French version by Rodolphe Gaillard

MODEST MOUSSORGSKY
(1839-1881)

Hoi! for the
Hoi! Hop, hop,

gay Ho - pak! Once I loved a fine Cos - sack!
hop, dan - sons! J'ai pour ma - ri un co - sa - que.

72136-8

72136-8

Down the sec-ond soft-ly slips; Off she trips to
puis au se-cond, un, deux, trois, Gai-ment les pieds

join the reels, With a young man at her heels. And old red pate,
s'a - gi-tent, la joy-eu-se s'é- -lan-ce Que le vieux chez

how she mocks him, When he calls she on- ly mocks him:
lui l'ap - pel - le, en ri- ant el - le ré - pond:—

"You old de-mon, now you're wed You must earn my dai- ly bread. That's what!
Pour ta fem-me tu m'as pri-se, com-me je suis, prends-moi donc! Hoi! hop!

72136-8

And the chil-dren you must feed, Clothe and give them what they need. That's how!
Toi gar-de bien la mai-son, Moi je veux a-voir la paix, Hoi! hop!

If you don't, see here, you'll rue it, For I'll find a way to do it, Heed that!
Tra-vail-le bien pour les en-fants et de mê-me pour ta fem-me, Hoi! hop!

Now be quick, you shame-less sin-ner, Find the mon-ey for our din-ner,
Ne les lais-se man-quer de rien, si non, gare à toi, mon a-mi!

Here now! If you will re-pen-tance show Rock the cra-dle
Hoi! hop! Et, mon vieux, fais at-ten-tion, dou-ce-ment ber-

to and fro,　　　So now!　　　Swing the cra - dle
ce l'en - fant,　　Hoi! hop!　　　A - fin de ne

slow - ly　　　To and fro,　　　So now!
pas　　　l'é - veil - ler,　　Hoi! hop!

Meno mosso

In the days when I was young-er,　Yes, and right pleas-ing, too!
Lors - que j'é - tais en - cor li - bre, sans sou - ci du len - de - main,

I would put a - way my a - pron　When my dai - ly toil was thro'
Ah! com - bien ri - ante et vi - ve, je cou - rais par les che - mins.

From my win-dow I'd nod smil-ing With my silks the time be-guil-ing_
A-vec cha-cun, *Ah! oui, vrai-ment,* *je m'a-mu-sais,* *tou-jours gaî-ment.*

f Più mosso

Come, my friends,you Johns and_ Si-mons! Go and don your coats, my fine ones.
Eh! là, Si-mon, Eh! là,_ I-van! Vite, en-trons et que l'on dan-se,

poco a poco accel.

Off we'll set_ in fin-est feath-er, Walk and talk and sing to-geth-er!
Et joy-eux_ le temps pas-se-ra, al-lons, bu-vons, que l'on chan-te!

Hoi! Hoi! Hoi! Hoi!
Hoi! Hop! Hoi! Hop!

Tempo I

Hoi! Hoi!__ Hoi! Hoi! Hoi! Hoi! For the gay Ho - pak!
Hoi! hoi,__ hoi, hoi, hoi, hoi, hop, hop, hop, dan - sons!

Once I loved a fine Cos - sack! Now he's old__ and__
J'ai pour ma - ri un co - sa - que, Il est vieux, il__

weak and ail - ing, Clum - sy, red__ of__ pate and fail - ing,
est bien u - sé, Et vrai - ment j'en__ suis las - sé - e,

That's my fate, too true, a - lack! Hoi!
j'aime mieux d'au - tres com - pa - gnons! Hoi!

To Alexander Sergeievich Dargomijsky

JEREMOUSCHKA'S CRADLE SONG

(Original Key)

Translated from the Russian
of NEKRASSOFF by Constance Purdy

MODEST MOUSSORGSKY
(1839-1881)

Adagio *Moderately slow*

VOICE

Bye - low, bye,___ bye,
(Ba - yon, baï,___ baï,)

PIANO

Bye - low, bye,_ bye,
(Ba - yon, baï,___ baï,)

Low - er than the ti - niest green grass-blade

Thou thy head must ev - er bend,

That the poor and hum - ble or - phan lad

ML-2904-3

Free from grief his life may spend. Bye-low, bye,_ bye, Bye-low, bye,_ bye.
(Ba - yon, baï,_ baï, Ba - yon, baï,_ baï.)

E - ven straws must break at might's_ com - mand,

So to might thy head bow low,_ And with all the great-est in _ the land_

Soon in fa - vor thou shalt grow. Bye-low, bye, bye, Bye-low, bye, bye.
(Ba - yon, baï, baï, Ba - yon, baï, baï.)

Lords and la-dies all thy friends shall be, Wealth and fame their court shall pay,

While with youth and beau-ty joy - ous - ly, Thou shalt jest the live-long day.

Gai - ly then thy life,__ free from care and strife, Hap-pi - ly__ shall roll a - way.

Bye-low, bye,__ bye, Bye-low, bye,__ bye.__
(Ba - yon, baï,__ baï, Ba - yon, baï,__ baï.)__

ML-2904-3